GIANT CHRISTMAS
FUN BOOK

HOW MANY BELLS CAN YOU FIND?

HOW MANY CHIMNEYS HAS FATHER CHRISTMAS GOT TO GO DOWN?

HOW MANY ELVES ARE WORKING OVERTIME?

HOW MANY STOCKINGS HAS FATHER CHRISTMAS GOT TO FILL?

HOW MANY PARCELS HAS FATHER CHRISTMAS GOT TO DELIVER?

HOW MANY CHRISTMAS BELLS ARE RINGING?

HOW MANY DIFFERENT THINGS ARE THERE TO EAT?

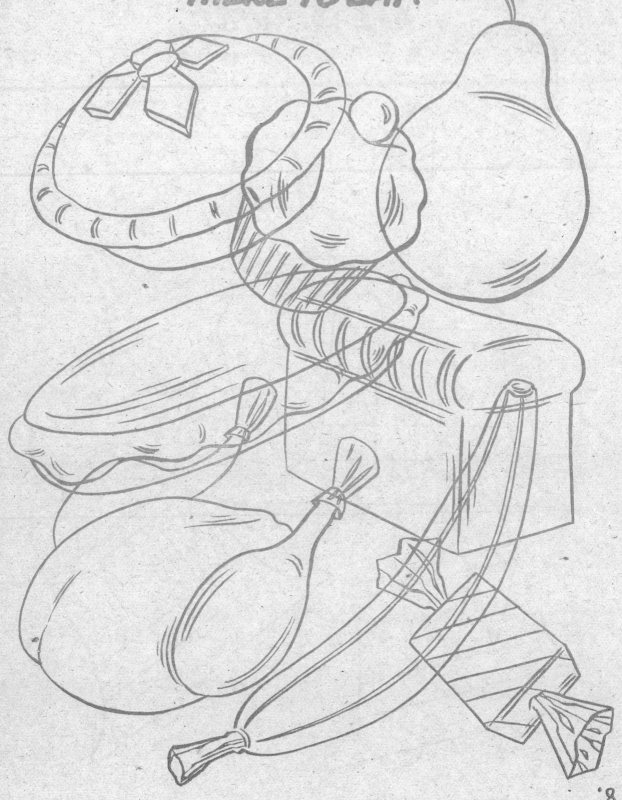

HOW MANY OBJECTS CAN YOU FIND THAT BEGIN WITH THE LETTER S?

NAME THE SMALLER PICTURES USING THE LETTERS FROM THE LARGE ONE

COWBOY HAT

NAME THE SMALLER PICTURES USING THE LETTERS FROM THE LARGE ONE

CAROL SINGERS

NAME THE SMALLER PICTURES USING THE LETTERS FROM THE LARGE ONE

PENCIL CASE

COLOUR THIS PICTURE

MISSING PIECE
Copy the right details into the correct space

MISSING PIECE

Copy the right details into the correct space

MISSING PIECE
Copy the right details into the correct space

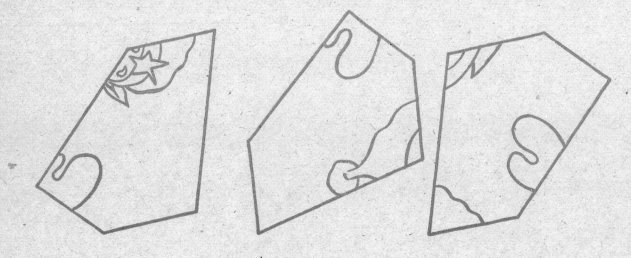

MISSING PIECE
Copy the right details into the correct space

COPY THE FACES ON TO THE EGGS

COPY THIS PICTURE IN THE SQUARES

WHAT WAS IN THE PARCEL ?

MY FIRST IS IN

BUT NOT IN - - - -

MY SECOND IS IN

BUT NOT IN - - - -

MY THIRD IS IN

BUT NOT IN - - - -

MY FOURTH IS IN

BUT NOT IN - - - -

SOAP

NUTTY NOUGHTS AND CROSSES

1. Find ten nuts. Five of one kind and five of another.
2. Instead of drawing noughts and crosses use the nuts like counters.
3. When you have finished playing, eat the nuts.

WHAT WAS IN THE PARCEL?

My first is in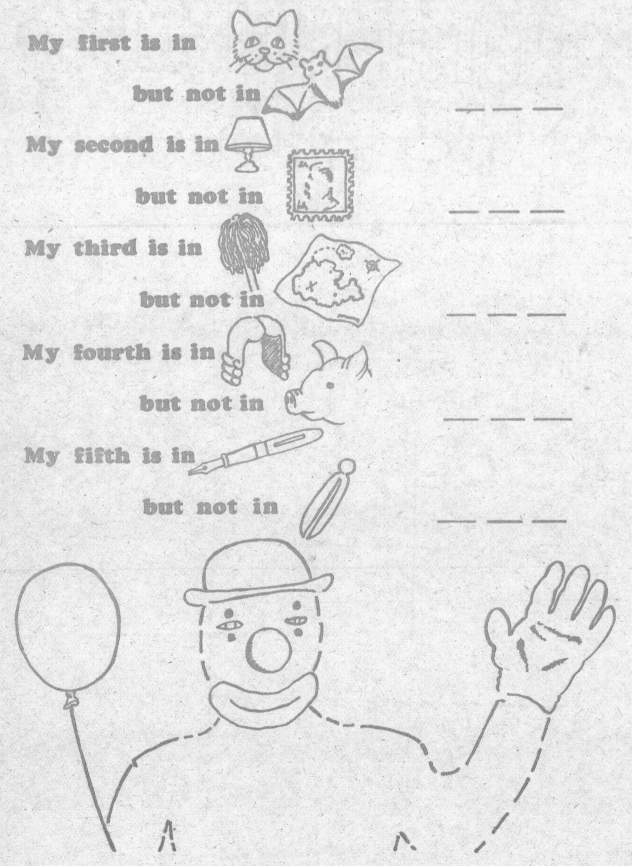

but not in

_ _ _

My second is in

but not in

_ _ _

My third is in

but not in

_ _ _

My fourth is in

but not in

_ _ _

My fifth is in

but not in

_ _ _

CHANGE ONE WORD INTO
ANOTHER changing one letter at a time
and making proper words as you do so

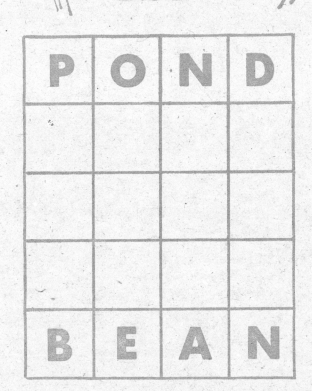

P	O	N	D
B	E	A	N

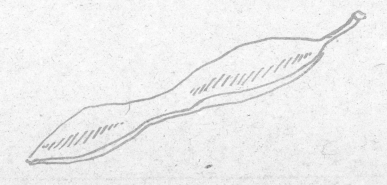

JOIN THE DOTS

What was in the box?

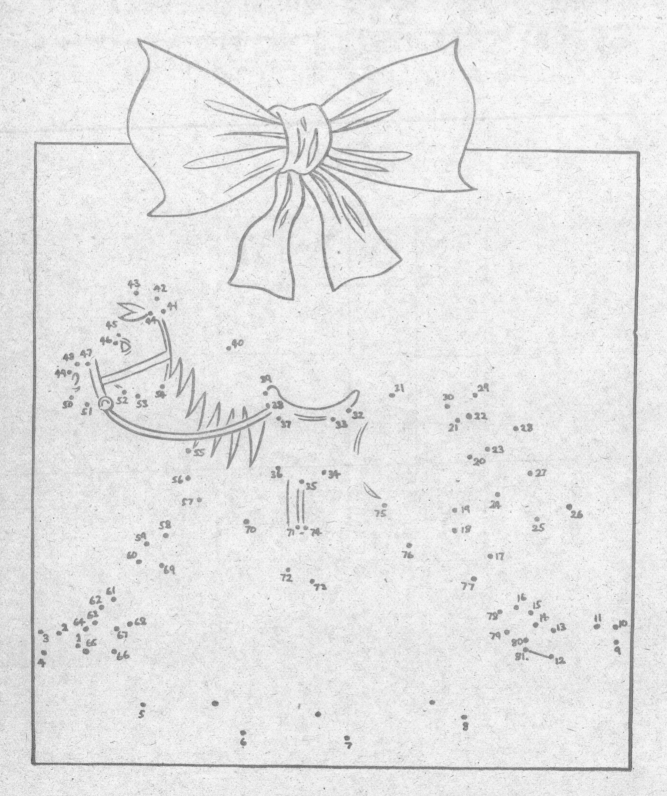

JOIN THE DOTS

Who was hiding behind the chair?

JOIN THE DOTS

Who ran away with the cracker?

JOIN THE DOTS

Who is hiding in the Christmas tree?

JOIN THE DOTS

What costume did John wear?

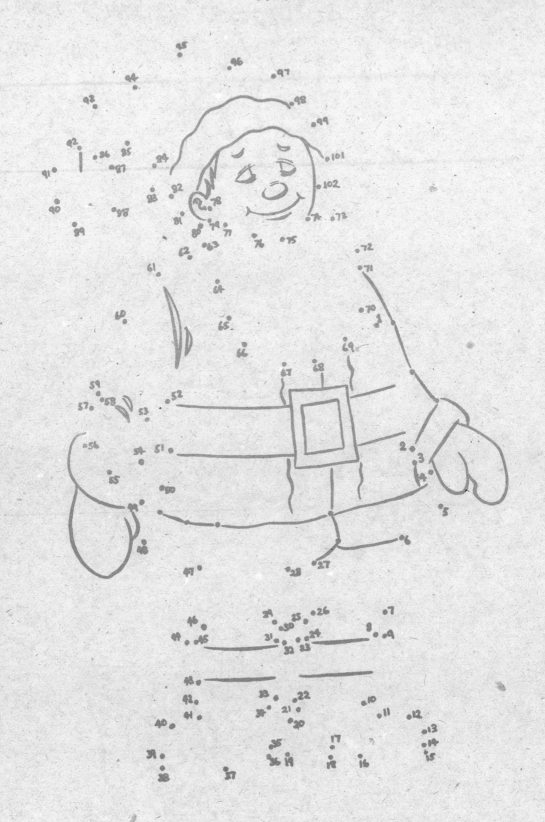

JOIN THE DOTS

Who is standing in the stable?

JOIN THE DOTS

What is standing under the Christmas tree?

JOIN THE DOTS

What is on the plate?

CAT and BIRD

A MODEL TO DECORATE
YOUR ROOM

TRACE AND TRANSFER
CAT ON TO CARDBOARD
AND CUT OUT WITH
HOLE IN TUMMY.

CUT OUT BIRD THE
SAME WAY AND
FIX TO CAT WITH
THREAD AND TAPE

COLOUR BOTH CAT
A BIRD ON BOTH
SIDES

HANG BY A LOOP
TAPED TO CAT'S HEAD

SIMPLE!

THE TWELVE DAYS OF CHRISTMAS

1. On the first day of Christ-mas my true love sent to me, a

part — ridge in a pear tree. 2. On the sec-ond

(repeat as appropriate)

five go — ld rings over →

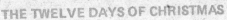

THE TWELVE DAYS OF CHRISTMAS

On the first day of Christmas
My true love sent to me
A partridge in a pear tree.

On the second day of Christmas
My true love sent to me
Two turtle doves
And a partridge in a pear tree.

On the third day of Christmas
My true love sent to me
Three French hens
Two turtle doves
And a partridge in a pear tree.

On the fourth day of Christmas
My true love sent to me
Four calling birds
Three French hens
Two turtle doves
And a partridge in a pear tree.

On the fifth day of Christmas
My true love sent to me
Five gold rings
Four calling birds
Three French hens
Two turtle doves
And a partridge in a pear tree.

On the sixth day of Christmas

My true love sent to me

Six geese a-laying

Five gold rings

Four calling birds

Three French hens

Two turtle doves

And a partridge in a pear tree.

On the seventh day of Christmas

My true love sent to me

Seven swans a-swimming

Six geese a-laying

Five gold rings

Four calling birds

Three French hens

Two turtle doves

And a partridge in a pear tree.

On the eighth day of Christmas

My true love sent to me

Eight maids a-milking

Seven swans a-swimming

Six geese a-laying

Five gold rings

Four calling birds

Three French hens

Two turtle doves

And a partridge in a pear tree.

On the ninth day of Christmas

My true love sent to me

Nine drummers drumming

Eight maids a-milking

Seven swans a-swimming

Six geese a-laying

Five gold rings

Four calling birds

Three French hens

Two turtle doves

And a partridge in a pear tree.

On the tenth day of Christmas

My true love sent to me

Ten pipers piping

Nine drummers drumming

Eight maids a-milking

Seven swans a-swimming

Six geese a-laying

Five gold rings

Four calling birds

Three French hens

Two turtle doves

And a partridge in a pear tree.

On the eleventh day of Christmas

My true love sent to me

Eleven ladies dancing

Ten pipers piping

Nine drummers drumming

Eight maids a-milking

Seven swans a-swimming

Six geese a-laying

Five gold rings

Four calling birds

Three French hens

Two turtle doves

And a partridge in a pear tree.

On the twelfth day of Christmas

My true love sent to me

Twelve lords a-leaping

Eleven ladies dancing

Ten pipers piping

Nine drummers drumming

Eight maids a-milking

Seven swans a-swimming

Six geese a-laying

Five gold rings

Four calling birds

Three French hens

Two turtle doves

And a partridge in a pear tree.

WHAT IS MISSING?
Write it in and add it to the drawing

A PARTRIDGE IN A Pe or TREE

WHAT IS MISSING?
Write it in and add it to the drawing

_____ TURTLE DOVES

WHAT IS MISSING?

Write it in and add it to the drawing

_ _ _ _ _ _

FRENCH HENS

WHAT IS MISSING?
Write it in and add it to the drawing

_ _ _ _ _ CALLING BIRDS

WHAT IS MISSING?
Write it in and add it to the drawing

_ _ _ _ _ GOLD RINGS

WHAT IS MISSING?

Write it in and add it to the drawing

_ _ _ _ GEESE A-LAYING

WHAT IS MISSING?
Write it in and add it to the drawing

_ _ _ _ _ _ _ SWANS A-SWIMMING

WHAT IS MISSING?
Write it in and add it to the drawing

_ _ _ _ _ _ MAIDS A-MILKING

WHAT IS MISSING?
Write it in and add it to the drawing

_____ DRUMMERS DRUMMING

WHAT IS MISSING?
Write it in and add it to the drawing

_____PIPERS PIPING

CODES
Each number represents a letter. Use this to find out what words the following make.

1	2	3	4	5	6	7	8	9	10	11	12	13	14	15	16	17	18	19	20	21	22	23	24	25	26
A	B	C	D	E	F	G	H	I	J	K	L	M	N	O	P	Q	R	S	T	U	V	W	X	Y	Z

1. 2, 5, 12, 12

_ _ _ _

2. 1, 14, 7, 5, 12

_ _ _ _ _

3. 19, 20, 1, 18

_ _ _ _

4. 3, 1, 14, 4, 12, 5

_ _ _ _ _ _

Now finish the drawings

1.

2.

3.

4.

SOLVE THE PUZZLE

by writing the names of the pictures and adding or subtracting letters according to the signs.

WHAT DID FATHER CHRISTMAS LEAVE BEHIND?

$- b + f + s +$

$- o + e + s =$

$- p =$

$- ba +$ $- lg =$

$- ail +$ $- l =$

SOLVE THE PUZZLE

by writing the names of the pictures and adding
or subtracting letters according to the signs

IT TAKES A LONG TIME:

− e =

w + − tin + − ig =

− c =

− ick + ri + − ick +

− p + s =

p + − c + c + − bl =

WHICH TWO ARE THE SAME?

1

2

3

4

5

SPOT THE DIFFERENCE:

There are 6 changes in the lower picture – Can you spot them?

SPOT THE DIFFERENCE:

There are 6 changes in the lower picture - Can you spot them?

SPOT THE DIFFERENCE:

There are 6 changes in the lower picture – Can you spot them?

SPOT THE DIFFERENCE:

There are 6 changes in the lower picture – Can you spot them?

SPOT THE DIFFERENCE:

There are 6 changes in the lower picture – Can you spot them?

Copy this
picture in
the squares —

Copy this picture in the squares

Copy this picture in the squares

Copy this picture in the squares —

Copy this picture in the squares —

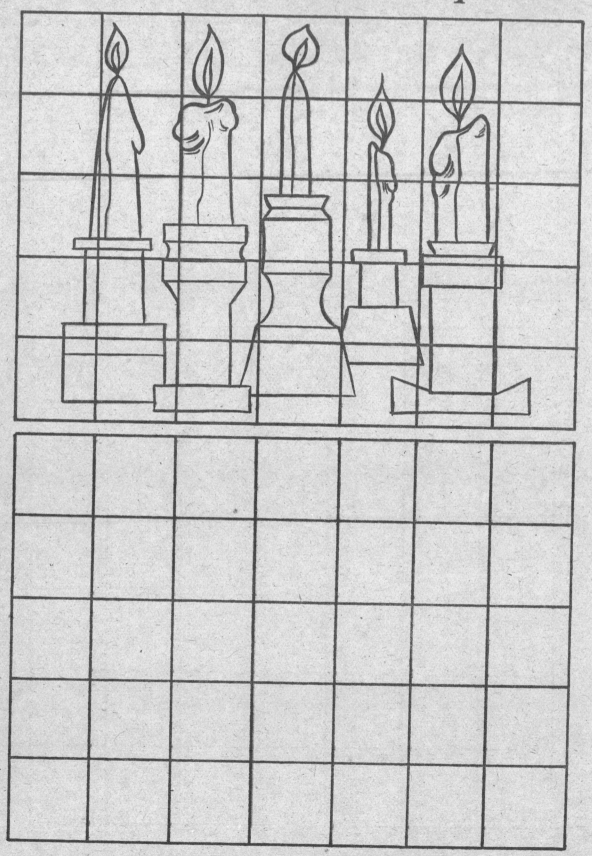

Copy this picture in the squares —

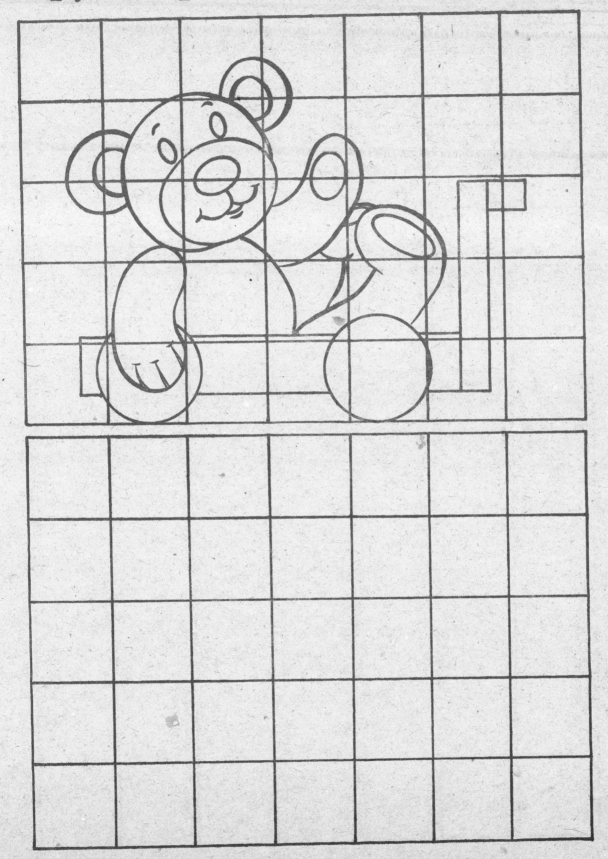

Copy this picture in the squares —

CHANGE THE LETTERS INTO SOMETHING TO EAT

CHRISTMAS PUDDING

CHANGE THE LETTERS INTO SOMETHING TO EAT

"CHESTNUTS"

CHANGE THE LETTERS INTO SOMETHING TO EAT

TURKEY

CHANGE THE LETTERS INTO SOMETHING TO EAT

MINCE PIE

USING THE FIRST LETTER FROM EACH PICTURE CAN YOU NAME WHAT THIS IS?

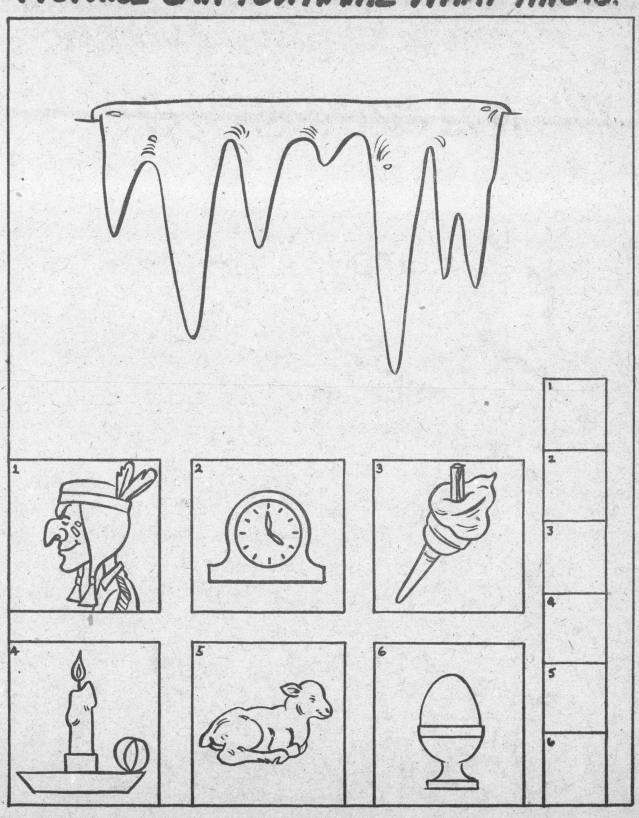

SOLVE THE PUZZLE

by writing the names of the pictures and adding
or subtracting letters according to the signs

THIS WILL SURPRISE YOU:

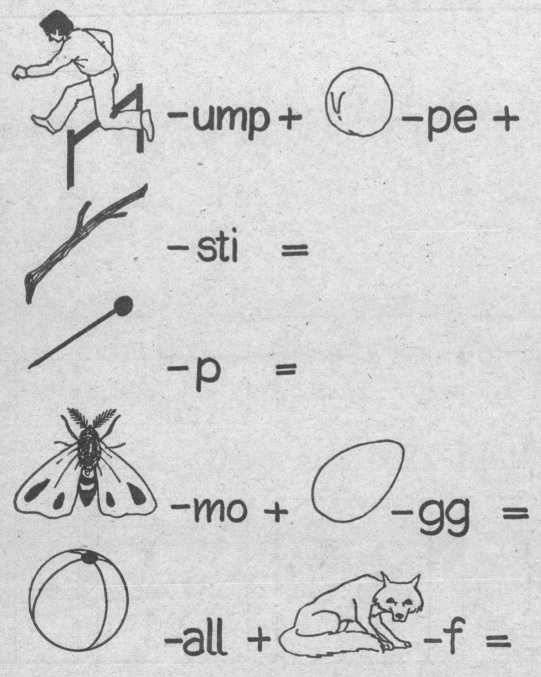

-ump +   -pe +

-sti =

-p =

-mo +   -gg =

-all +   -f =

SOLVE THE PUZZLE

by writing the names of the pictures and adding or subtracting letters according to the signs.

THESE MAKE A NOISE:

$-ow+y+m+$

$-g+l+s =$

$-h =$

$-thb+s =$

SOLVE THE PUZZLE

by writing the names of the pictures and adding or subtracting letters according to the signs.

THIS CAN DANCE:

–ht =

–py + –a +

–t =

– ste =

–nt

–ipe + –r =

FIND SOME BUTTONS AND AN EMPTY EGG BOX AND MAKE YOURSELF A GAME

Use the bottom half of an empty egg box. Draw a number (from 1 to 6) in the bottom of each section.

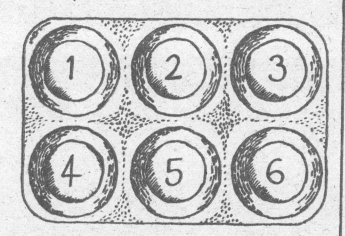

Find six small buttons and one large one for each player. Use the large button to flick the small ones into the box.

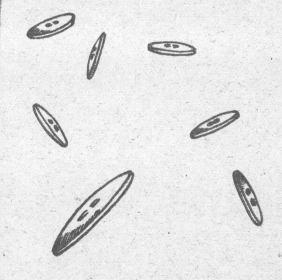

Take turns. When one player has got all his small buttons in the eggbox the game is finished. Each button scores the number Add up the score. The player with the highest score wins.

COPY THE FACES ON TO THE EGGS

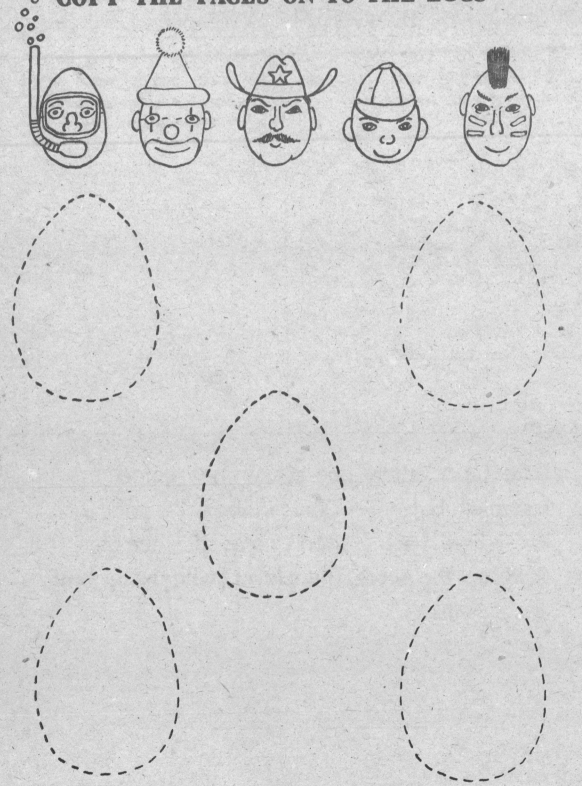

CHANGE ONE WORD INTO ANOTHER CHANGING ONE LETTER AT A TIME AND MAKING PROPER WORDS AS YOU DO SO

B	E	L	T
N	E	S	T

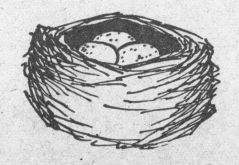

CHANGE ONE WORD INTO ANOTHER CHANGING ONE LETTER. AT A TIME AND MAKING PROPER WORDS AS YOU DO SO

CHANGE ONE WORD INTO ANOTHER CHANGING ONE LETTER AT A TIME, AND MAKING PROPER WORDS AS YOU DO SO.

COPY THE FACES ON TO THE EGGS

PAINT THE PICTURE
and send it as a Christmas card

MERRY CHRISTMAS

PAINT THE PICTURE using the key

1-WHITE 2-BLUE 3-YELLOW 4-PINK 5-RED 6-BROWN

RHYMING COUPLES

Join the dots.

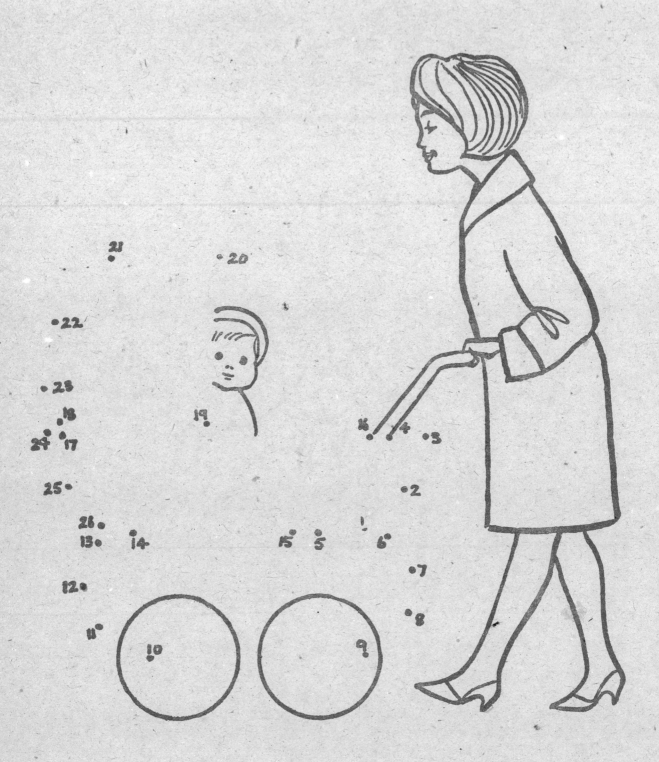

Colour this sunset
scene

Can you name these flowers?

SQUEE! WHAT'S THAT?
HELP!

What can he be so scared of? Join the dots and see. Then colour the completed picture as nicely as you can.

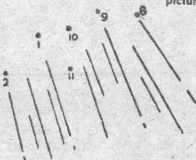

COLOUR CODE   1-ORANGE 2-RED 3-BLUE
4-WHITE 5-YELLOW 6-BLACK

Birthday Candles

Can you put the name of each of the five children on to their own cakes? Tom is six; Joan is eight; Jill is ten; Sam in seven and Linda is four years old.

Join the dots and name the animal.

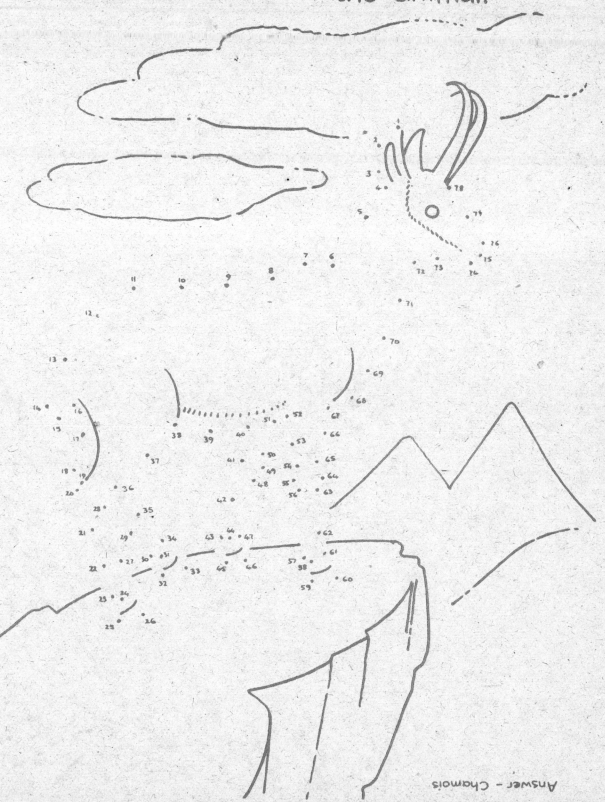

Answer – Chamois

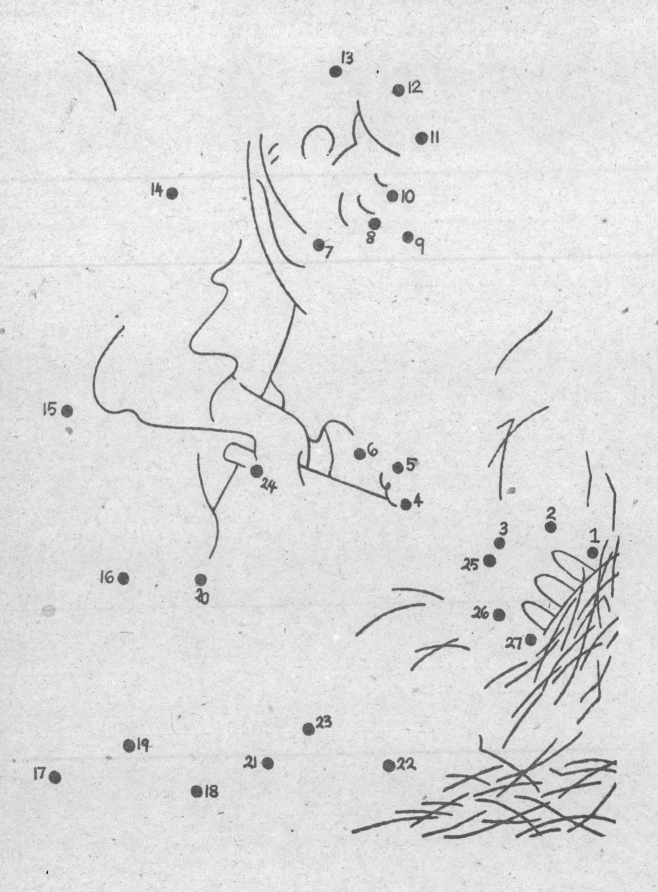

Make this Origami HOUSE
in simple step by step stages.

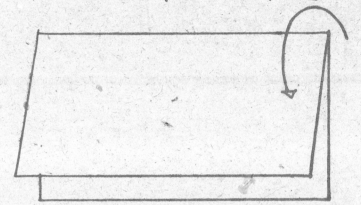

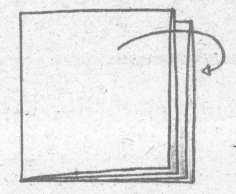

1. Fold downwards..
   in half.

2 Then fold
   in half again.

Take a piece of thin paper
like this, then follow the
instructions.

You
can
build
your
own
House!

See the next
page.

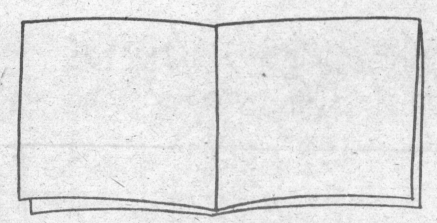

3. Keep the paper in the same position
---then unfold, like this.

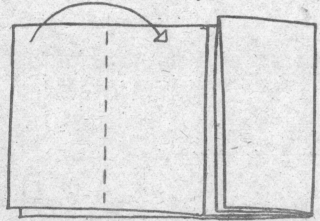

4. Then fold the sides to the centre
as shown.

5. Look carefully, your paper should
now look like this.

6. Unfold the paper - like this.

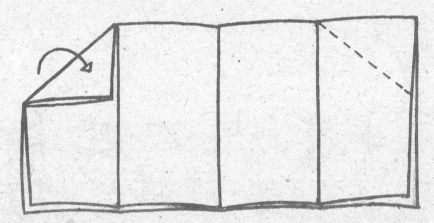

7. Make folds at the top corners, like this. Then comes the tricky bit!

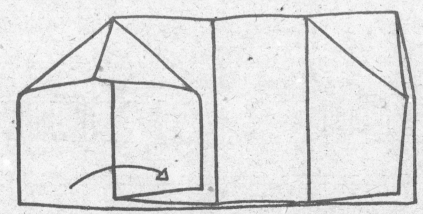

8. Fold the top layer into the centre as shown. Repeat on the other side.

10. This is what you should have now.

Draw windows and doors. Colour the roof red etc..

Colour this picture - then paste your Origami house in place.

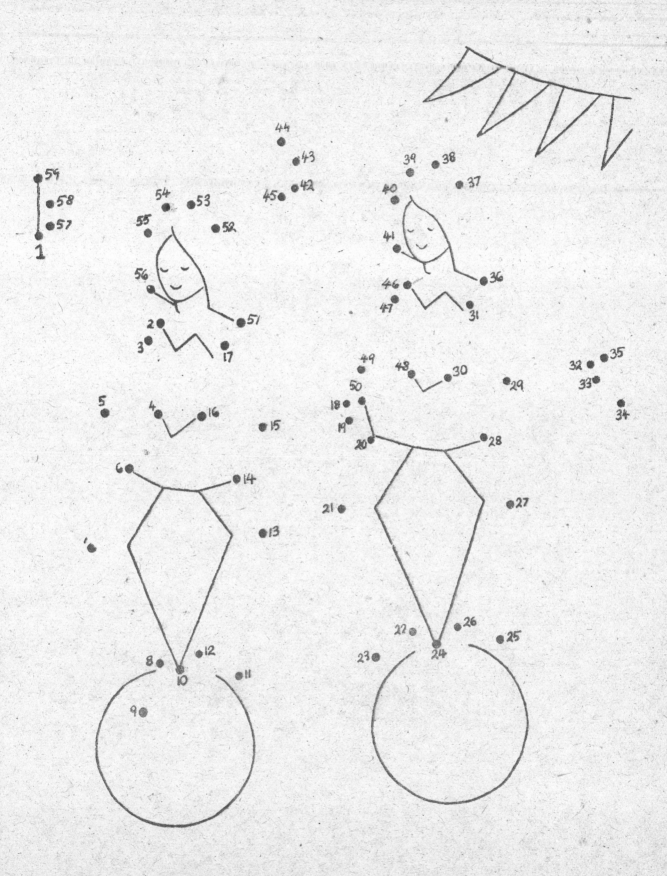

"I like you," says Tibby

Complete the picture by joining the dots, then colour it brightly.

Mixed Shadows

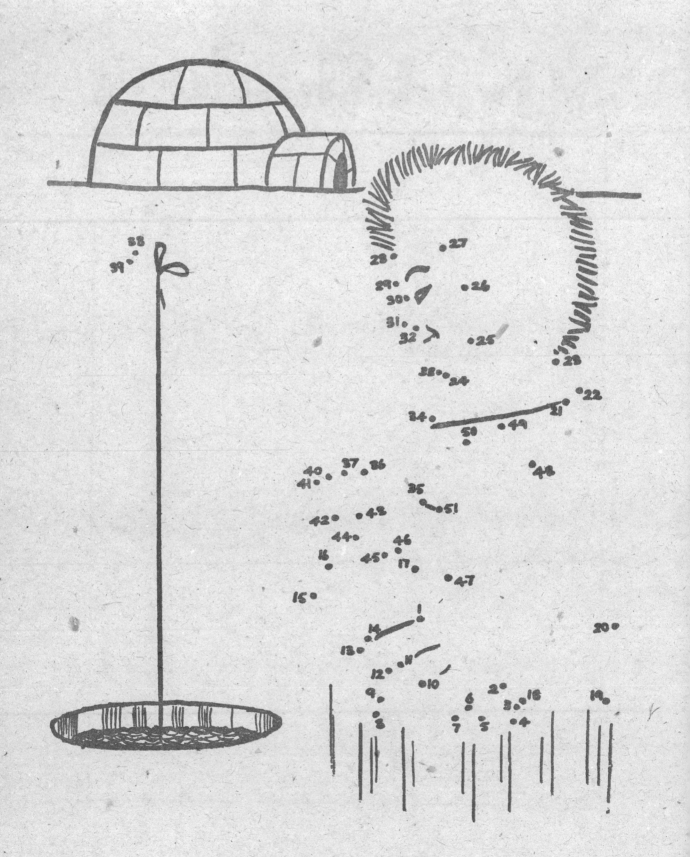

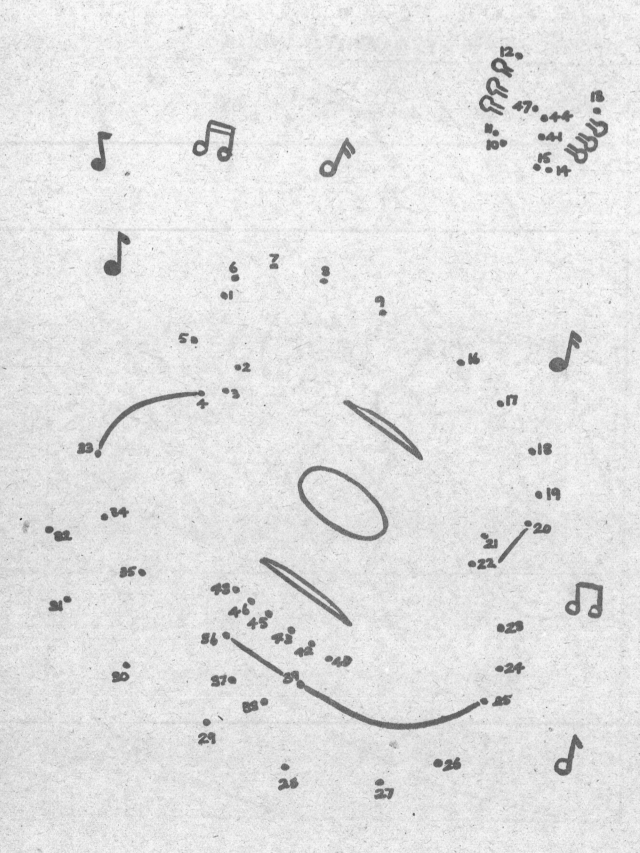

Colour the MAN WITH THE PNEUMATIC DRILL

What was in the fairy wood?

Just join the dots, and see for yourself.

Write the first letter of each
object in the spaces to find
a girls name.

Which Box is different?

Can you spot which Box is different from the others?

COLOUR CODE 1-ORANGE 2-BLUE 3-YELLOW
4-RED 5-BROWN 6-BLACK

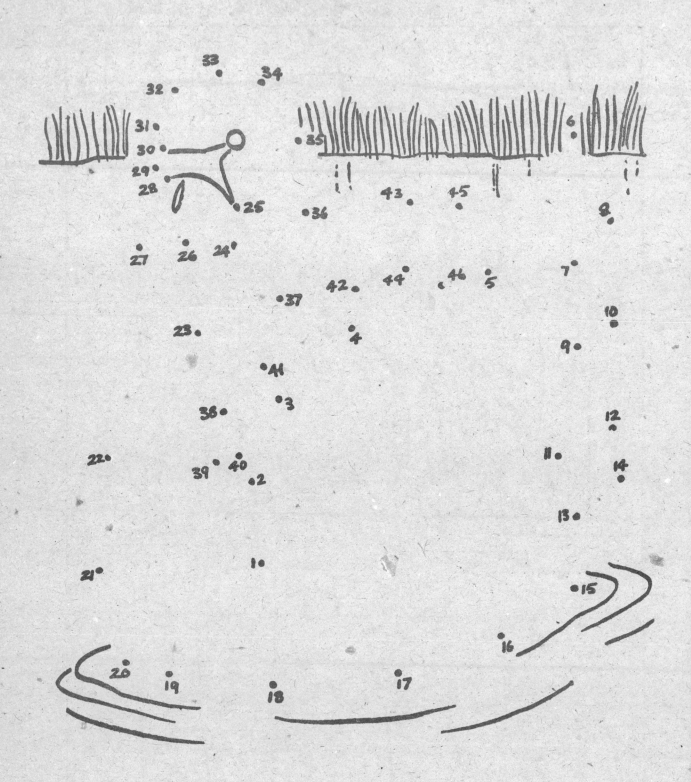

Stitch·a·Story

Prick holes at the dots. Colour the design with crayons. Then sew round the outline with coloured wool or cottons.

When you are young and very short - it's a nuisance! You can't see what's on the table.

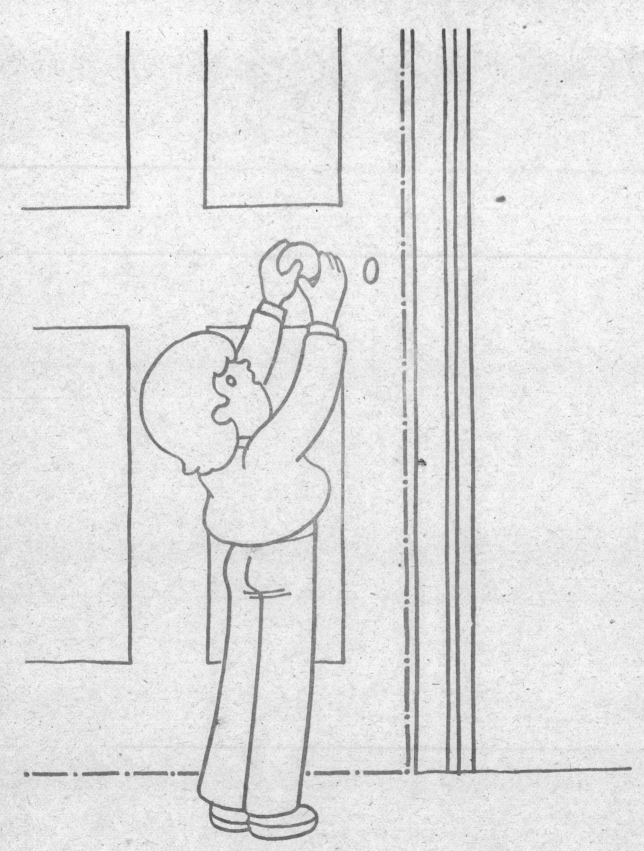

You can't open doors very easily.

1838 A London Postman.

AD 1927. What do you think of
these clothes?

1979 AD Skinhead and Punk.
Colour these clothes.

Little Shadowshow

MOTH

RABBIT

Let us draw some Faces!

Make up your faces. One is drawn here to show you how.

An easy Puzzle Picture

Fill in the blank squares to complete this picture of an Ostrich.

Draw a Steam Engine !

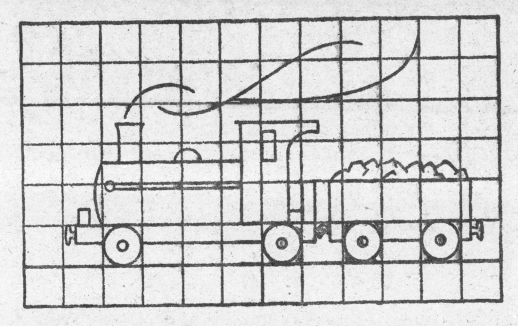

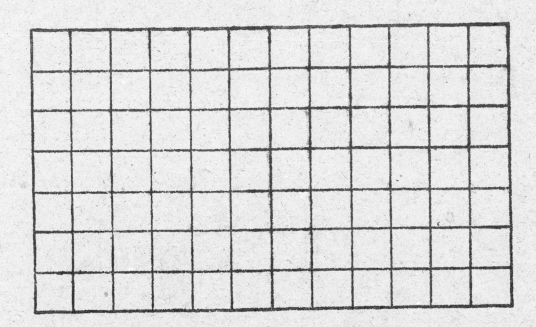

Copy this picture in the squares below.

Which House is different?

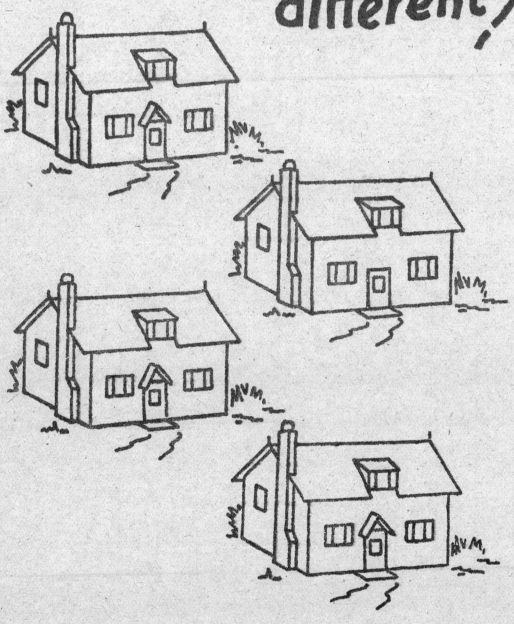

Can you spot which house is different from the others?

Designs to draw & paint

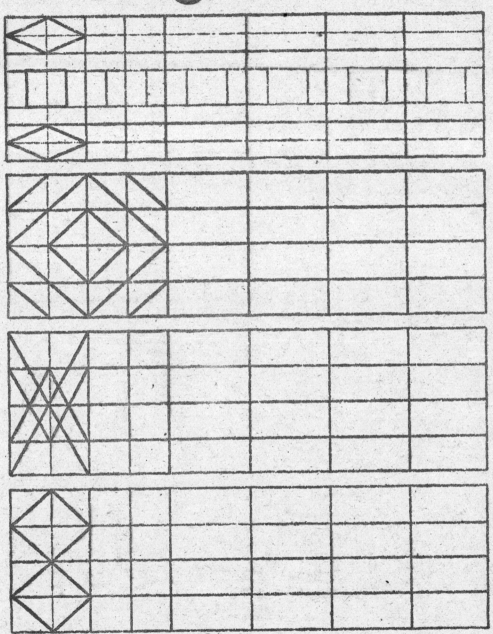

Copy these designs or make up your own. It would be good fun
to colour these desings

A Picture Crossword

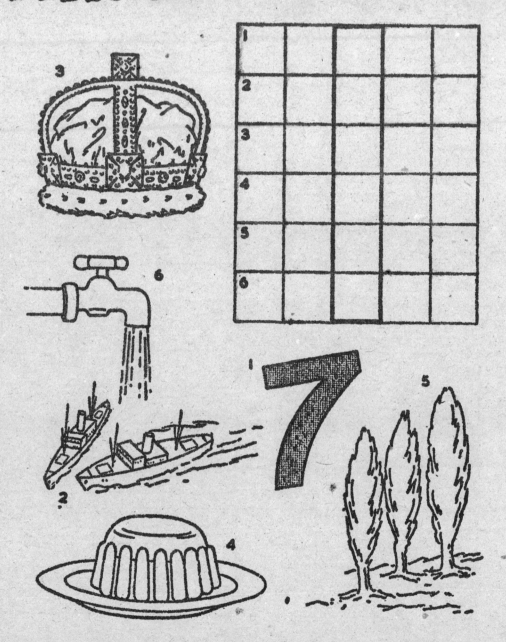

A WELL-KNOWN FLOWER

What are the children doing?

Join the dots from 1 to 10 and see what kind of holiday the children are having.

WHOSE HAT?

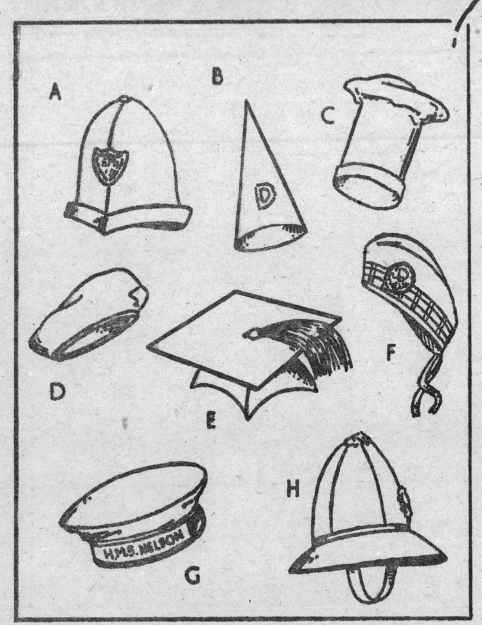

A

B

C

D

E

F

G

H.M.S. NELSON

H

Can you guess who wears these hats?

The Windmill

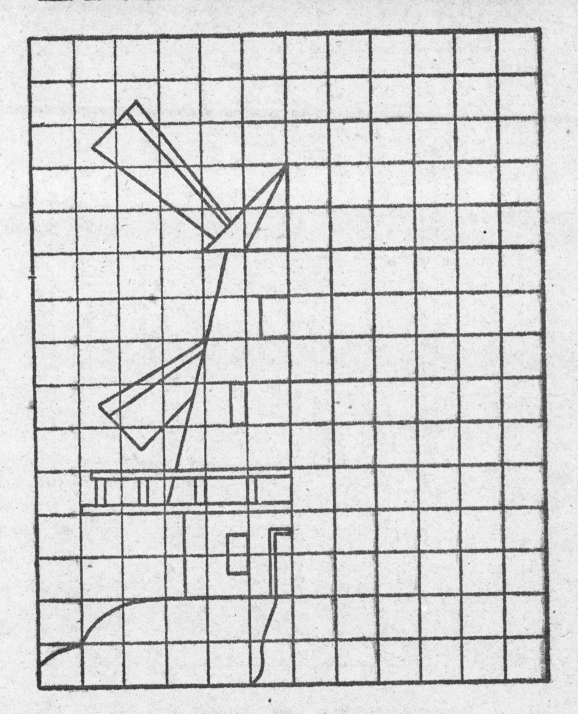

Draw the other half of the Windmill, then colour it.

What is on the Larder shelves?

Somebody teased Mother by mixing up the names on the things in the larder. Can you find out what is in each of the jars or packets?

Treasure Chest

Draw the Treasure Chest by joining the dots from 1 to 10. You could colour the different pieces of jewellery and make quite a pretty picture.

Join the dots.

THE RUN-AWAY ICE-CREAM CART

Join the dots to complete this happy picture, then paint it all in gay colours.

Colour the One Man Band

Which Path did Sammy take to get home?

Start here

A Puzzle for the very little ones.

Complete this drawing, then colour it with bright colours.

Pictures to draw

Copy each of these pictures in the opposite square.

The Great Stilt Race!

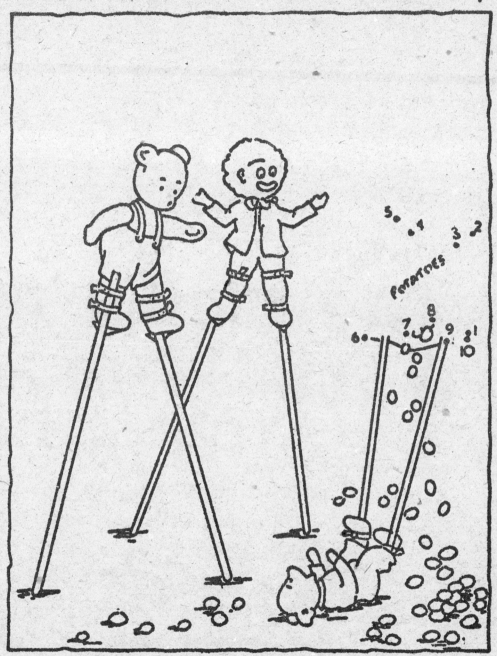

WHAT TRIPPED HIM UP?

THE HANGING BASKET

Draw the flowers by joining the dotted lines — then colour the picture.

Now make this Origami PIG

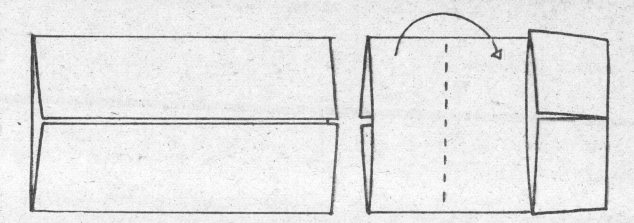

1. Fold the top and bottom edge to the centre.

2. Turn the paper over & fold the sides to the centre.

Turn to the next page.

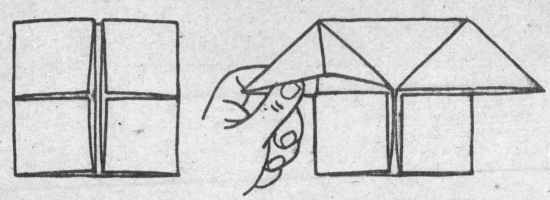

3. This is where you should be by now.

4 Pull out the top flaps as if making a "roof."

5. Now pull out the bottom flaps in the same way.

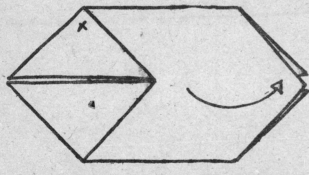

6. Now fold the right hand flap over to the right as shown.

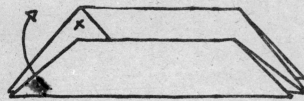

7. Now fold in half - carefully.

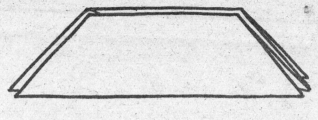

8. This is what you should have by now.

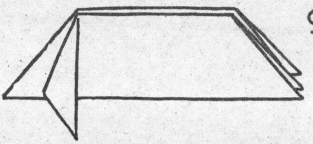

9. Fold the left hand corner to make a leg.

10. Do the same on the other side.

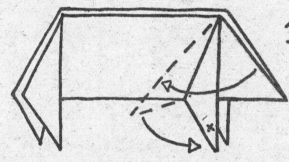

11 Fold the right-hand corner back and fold forward to make front legs.

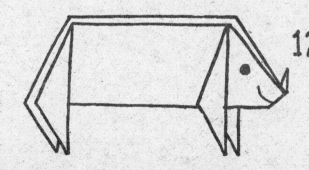

12 Make a nose like this. Then draw the pigs face.

turn to the next page.

Now colour this picture of the pigs sty, then you can paste your pig in it.

Find the Nursery rhyme

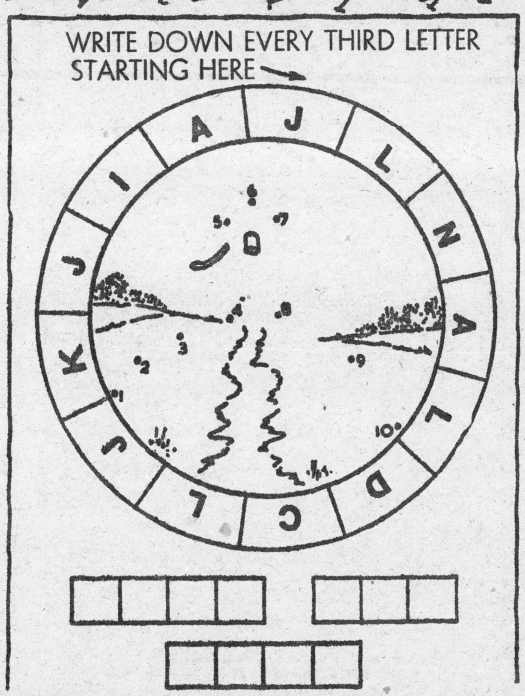

WRITE DOWN EVERY THIRD LETTER STARTING HERE →

What was in the Pond?

This is a little more difficult than usual. Join the dots on the
f i v e   different sets, starting each set from the figure 1 and
following the arrow.

Fun on the Pool

What are they playing on? Join the dots, and see.

COLOUR CODE   1-BLUE 2-LIGHT BLUE
3-RED 4-WHITE

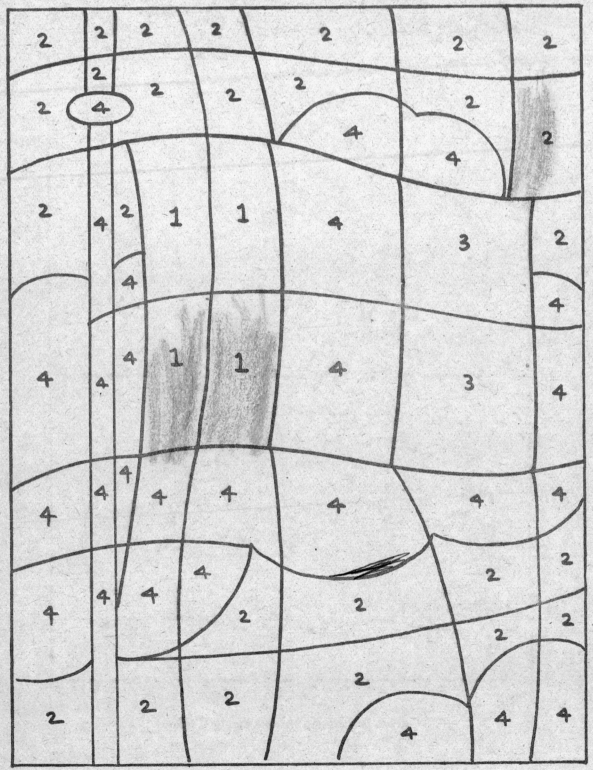